Ex Libris

ISBN 0-439-33168-4

Illustrations copyright © 2000 by Christopher Bing. All rights reserved. Published by Scholastic Inc., 555 Broadway, New York, NY 10012, by arrangement with Handprint Books. SCHOLASTIC and associated logos are trademarks and/or registered trademarks of Scholastic Inc.

12 11 10 9 8 7 6 5 4 3 2   1 2 3 4 5 6/0

Printed in Mexico

49

First Scholastic printing, September 2001

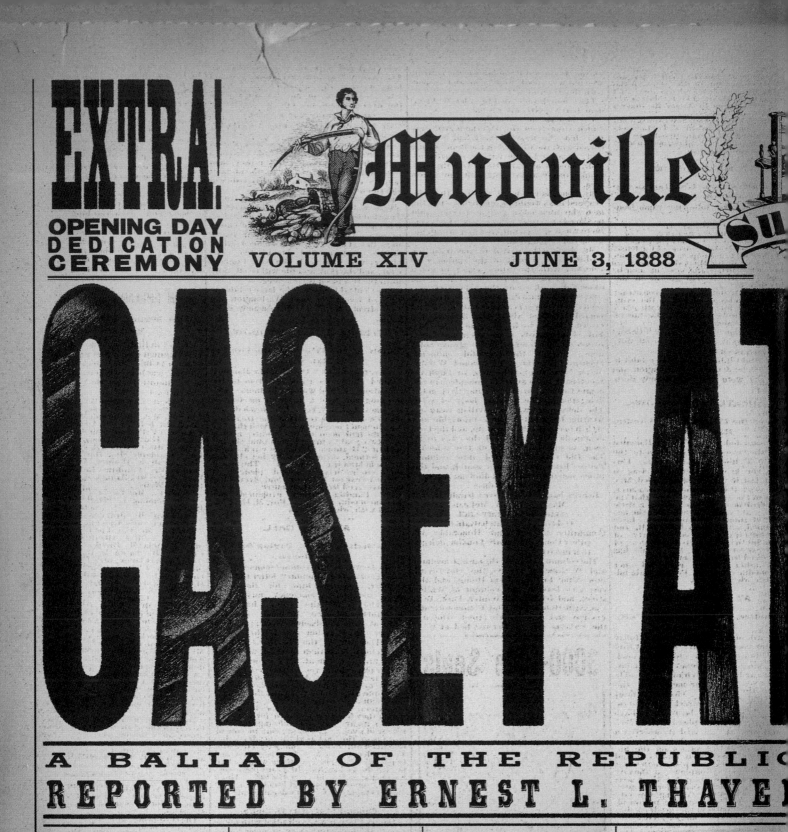

EXTRA!

OPENING DAY DEDICATION CEREMONY

Mudville

VOLUME XIV   **JUNE 3, 1888**

CASEY AT

A BALLAD OF THE REPUBLIC

REPORTED BY ERNEST L. THAYER

THIS BOOK IS DEDICATED to all those children of spring who have found moments of heaven in the smell of a freshly mowed ballpark beneath their feet, a well-worn and oiled glove on their hand, the crack of a bat on a ball and the umpire's bellow of "Play Ball," but most especially Bill, Gil, Sean, Patrick, Ryan, Ryan O., Matt, Matty, William, Biff, and Christian.

This book is for my son Christian, for giving me back a love thought lost for the game of baseball, and the cherished gift of watching the greatest catch in the history of baseball on a warm spring night in 1995. And for my wife, Wendy, and our daughters, Amy and Tessa, for their patience while I juggled furiously, standing on one foot.

A NOTE TO THE READER...

...about the second signature on the illustrations which appears in the lower right hand corner of each spread.

Until late in the 19th century, the metal plates from which newspaper illustrations were printed were prepared by hand by craftsmen known as engravers. Their skill lay in translating the light and shadows of the artist's original drawing on paper into the precise, unforgiving line cut into zinc or copper plates. Some of these engravers were merely crude copyists, others displayed keen talent and an interpretive gift which often augmented the artist's intention (and even covered his

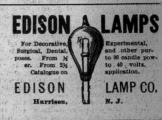
flaws). Over time, several of the engravers became famous in their own right, and their work was sought after as that of the artist whose images they reproduced. It was custom for the original artist's name to appear in the lower left of the engraving; the engraver's name, when allowed, appeared in the lower right.

(Continued on front end papers)

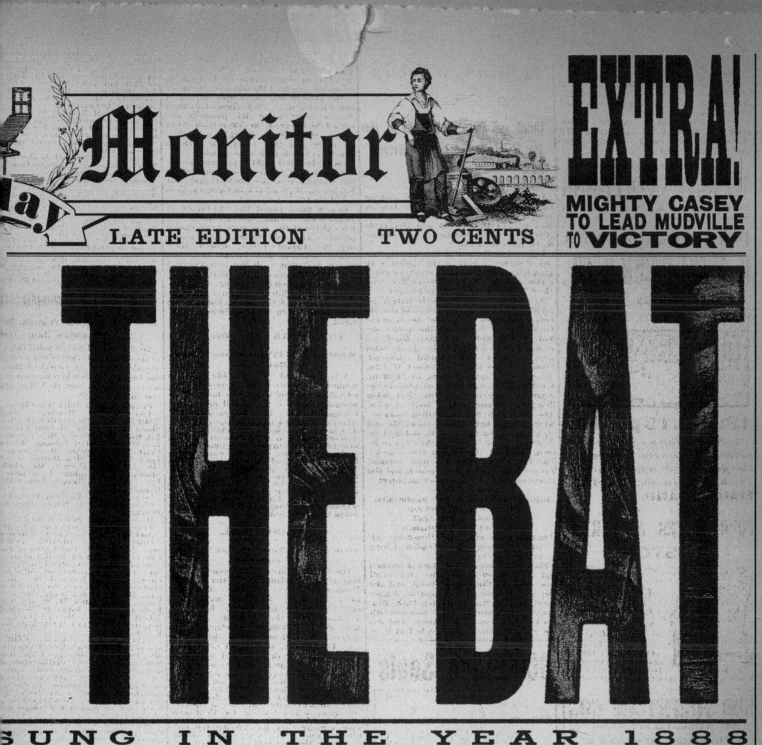

Monitor

LATE EDITION **TWO CENTS**

THE BAT

SUNG IN THE YEAR 1888
ILLUSTRATED BY CHRISTOPHER BING

THANKS & ACKNOWLEDGEMENTS

Martin Gardner's brilliant and entertaining *The Annotated Casey at the Bat* is the source for the title and stanzas in this version of Casey, which is exactly how it was first published Sunday morning, June 3rd, 1888 in the *San Francisco Examiner*.

Wallace Tripp's wonderfully illustrated version (Coward, McCann and Geoghegan, Inc., New York) in 1978 was/is the inspiration for this version and should be print again.

This book (and those to follow) would not have happened without the moral support and a helpful word on my behalf by Dr. Henry Louis Gates Jr.

Carl Brandt, my agent, for listening to the helpful word and stepping out of his usual arena and into another on my behalf, and being more interested in my getting it right than the many deadlines that came and went (due to family needs), and the bottom line (and his son, who has fought for me in another artistic arena for years helping to support my venture into this one, none of us knowing, until recently, of our professional relationships with each other).

Christopher Franceschelli, my publisher, who backed this rookie and believed in this book since he first saw sketches eight years ago.

My wife, Wendy, and our children, who have to beware of the bear in the barn, but they keep feeding it anyway, and spend so much time going without.

My parents who keep a hope and faith (in me) alive that would put Boston Red Sox or Chicago Cubs fans to shame.

My in-laws who actually admit that I'm family, and Gil Barrett (my brother-in-law) who put up with my turning him from the best mechanic in New England into THE model for Casey. Finding the world of modeling too dull, he has happily returned to being the best mechanic in New England.

Joseph and Princes Fludd who gave me friendship, food, and shelter one very cold and snowy night on my way to do research at the Baseball Hall of Fame.

The Baseball Hall of Fame in Cooperstown, New York and all the people who work in their photo

(Continued on front end papers)

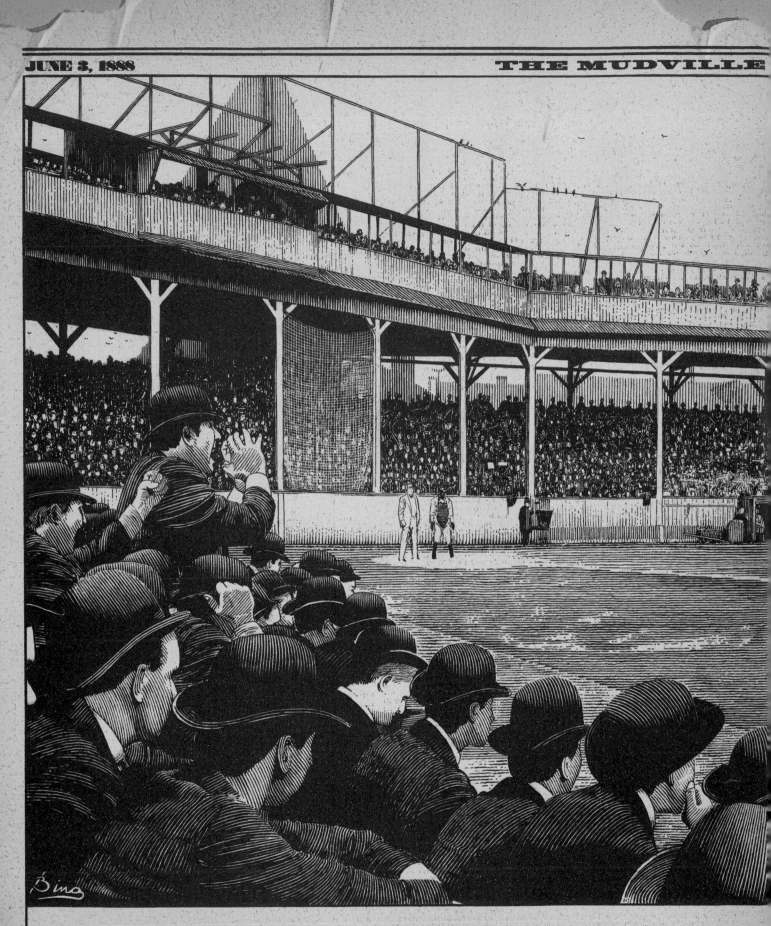

The outlook wasn't brilliant for the Mudville nine that day;
The score stood four to two with but one inning more to play.

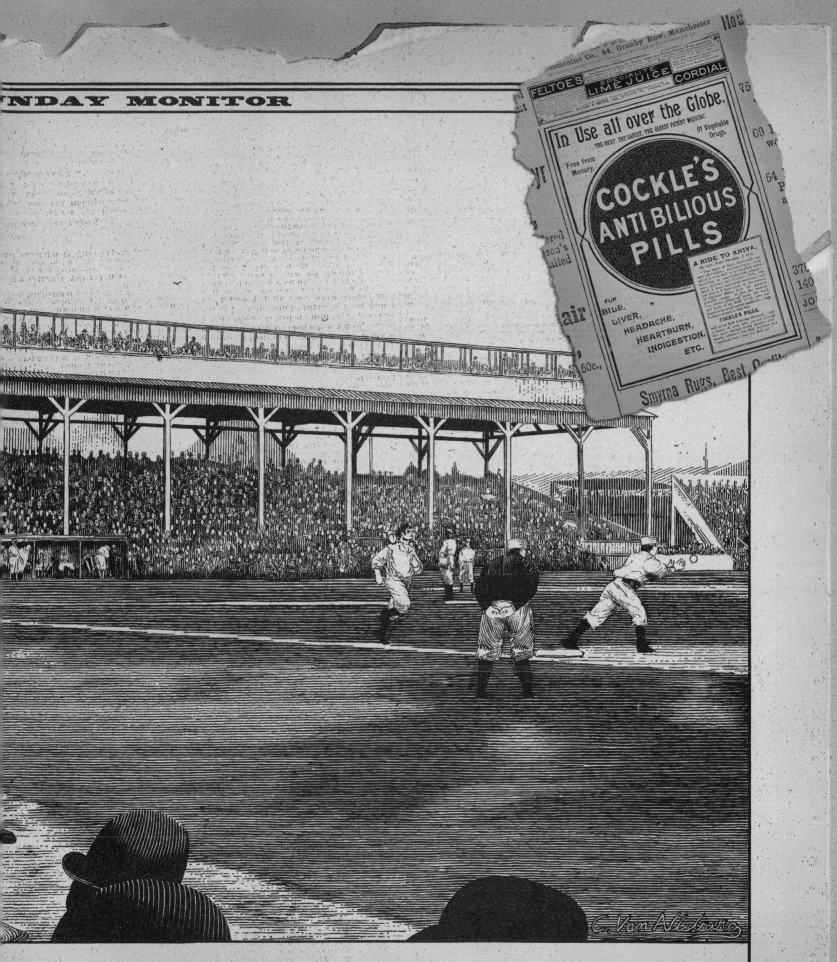

And then when Cooney died at first, and Barrows did the same,
A sickly silence fell upon the patrons of the game.

ess themselves as delighted with their tion and that everything seen in rich exceeds their expectations.

the boat last night a pleasant episode an elegant banquet complimentary to committee of the Ancients and their isle guests, tendered by George L. Con-

after which all present knelt while a wedding hymn was sung. Mendelssohn's wedding march was played as the couple left the church.

A reception was held at the residence of Mrs. Nathaniel W. Curtis, on Beacon street, after the ceremony.

Among those who were present were: Mrs. N. W. Curtis, Mr. Ag on,

CUSTOMS DECISIONS.

Two Circulars from Washington Received by the Collector.

This forenoon the following came from Washington:

has concurred with the Board of Aldermen upon the appropriation bill rather than stop public business caused by the obstructionists of the board—eight Republican aldermen—it is

Resolved, That the appropriation bill, as it was originally sent to the Board of Alder-

A straggling few got up to go in deep despair. The rest
Clung to that hope which springs eternal in the human breast;

They thought if only Casey could but get a whack at that—
We'd put up even money now with Casey at the bat.

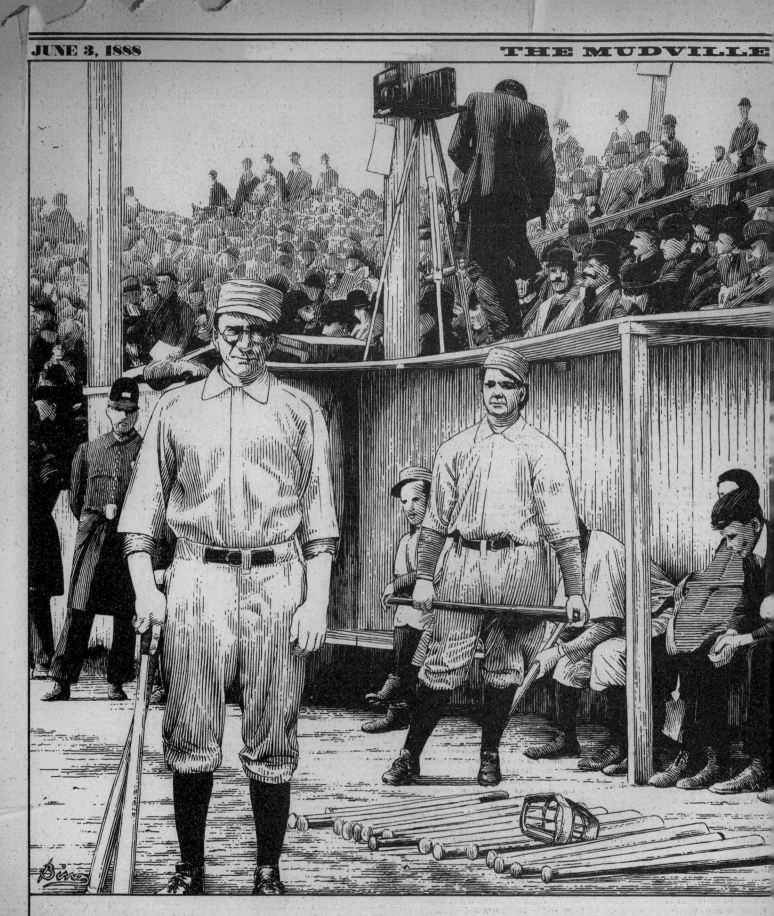

But Flynn preceded Casey, as did also Jimmy Blake,
And the former was a lulu and the latter was a cake;

about what is going to happen than all the Californians, Oregonian. Nevadians and the rest of the Pacific slopers now here will know after the happening shall have happened. Still, Mr. Gorman is not communistic enough to share his superior information with the weary corridor throngs. He would only say:

"I came here to listen to Indiana in the matter of the vice-presidency. If however

M. Gilkison, Augustus L. Priest, H. S. Turner, John T. Davis, F. M. Cruuden, C. H. Sampson, H. W. L. Thatcher, H. W. Williams. New Hampshire, John W. O'Connell, chairman; B. Finney, R. H. Hubbard, Clinton B. Powell, vice chairman; J. J. Emerson, Bennett Pike, M. J. Kenefick, Rhode Island, Edward D. Landers, chairman; John D. En-

of the coming campaign. This nomination I never sought, and did not want; but now that I have accepted it, I shall do all in my power to promote the best interest of my party. Why Mr. Clifford declined to run I do not know; there is no dissension, ill-feeling or bad blood in the ranks of the first district Democrats that I am aware of. So far as the presidential election is con-

ing. Dr. Thayer was called and pronounced it a case of heart trouble. The remains were taken in charge by Undertaker Manning of Albany street.

—An alarm from box 9 was rung in at midnight for a slight fire in the rear of building at 49 Charter street, occupied by Michael Gannon. The fire was caused by the upsetting of a kerosene lamp.

SURGING FANS SPARK NEAR RIOT
SCORE CAST IN DOUBT WHEN BALL ROLLS INTO CROWD
MANAGERS AND CITY OFFICIALS RENEW CRY FOR BUILDING OF OUTFIELD FENCES

Richloam--Saturday, June 2

Martin Stone's slam into left looked to be a solid double for the Mudville nine in yesterday afternoon's game against the Richloam Roosters. Then the ball hit an obstruction in the grass and began rolling towards the crowd watching from the sidelines. Some twenty Mudville fans crossed onto the field, placed the ball into protective custody and physically prevented Regis Smallwood, the Rooster's leftfielder, from apprehending the ball.

Richloam fans were understandably incensed and exercised swift revenge, attacking the visiting Mudville fans with a flurry of walking sticks. At least one Mudville fan was seen hobbling off the field with a bloodied shirt and blackened eye. Only the quick action of the local constab-

MAYOR STONE VOICES OUTRAGE

The incident prompted Mayor Sam Stone to make a renewed call for the erection of a wall separating fans from the field. While such a barrier would be a novelty to the game--rumor has it that something of the sort has been built in New York--it is hoped that this action might lead to greater crowd safety and less confusion on the field. More than one fan, however, was heard to say that an artificial barricade would severely curtail the enjoyment of the dance. On

So upon that stricken multitude grim melancholy sat,
For there seemed but little chance of Casey's getting to the bat.

THE COVER

But Flynn let drive a single, to the wonderment of all,
And Blake, the much despis-ed, tore the cover off the ball;

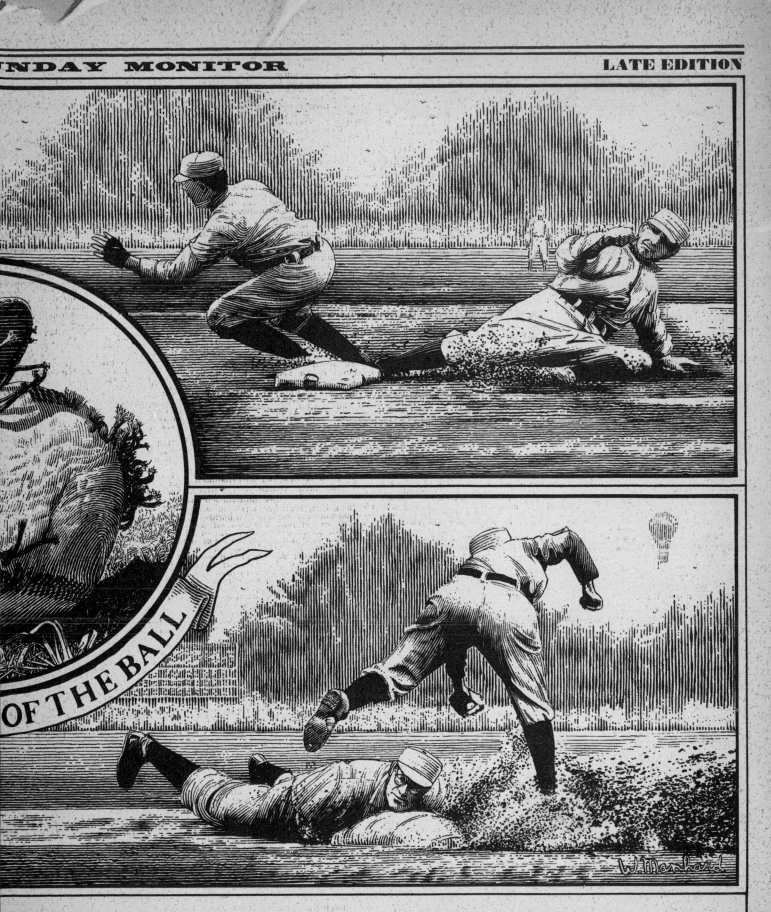

OF THE BALL

W. Manhard

And when the dust had lifted, and the men saw what had occurred,
There was ~~Johnnie~~ safe at second and Flynn a-hugging third.

Jimmy

same combination, and Cleveland is
the United States Senate for one te
he died, with his mind all shattered, in
possession of a city office.
understand that Mrs. Blair is still living
e with a grown up family of ver we i
rded sons and daughters, but that she
been poor until the government re-
tly gave her a pension, after long wait-

now pending in Congress should be mentioned in the platform. By such people it
is thought to be sufficient squarely to in-
dorse the message of the President and
earnestly urge upon Congress the execution
of the principle. The New York platform
is really liked by Mr. Cleveland bet-
ter than that of our

PROOFREADER SOUGHT

THE MUDVILLE MONITOR seeks proofreader for immediate hire due to last
incumbent's sudden departure. The successful
candidate shall possess an exquisite command
of the language, display meticulous attention
to detail while working to extreme deadlines,
be impervious to the bustle of a cacophonous

in their power.'

Kansas Men Favor Gresham.

TOPEKA, Kan., June 2.—A canvass of the
18 delegates from Kansas to the Chicago
convention since Mr. Blaine's last
letter shows that Gresham is the
personal preference of the ma-

Then from 5,000 throats and more there rose a lusty yell;
It rumbled through the valley, it rattled in the dell;

C. C. Brandt

It knocked upon the mountain and recoiled upon the flat,
For Casey, mighty Casey, was advancing to the bat.

Base Balls for Boys.

Cheap and well made, leather covered

Base Ball Bats.

Base Ball Caps.

There was ease in Casey's manner as he stepped into his place;
There was pride in Casey's bearing and a smile on Casey's face.

ITOR

THE NATIONAL SPORTS REPOR[TING]
GAZETT[E]
THE PROUD VOICE OF THE GENTLEMAN ATHLE[TE]
AND AMATEUR SPORTSMAN THROUGHOUT THE LAN[D]

PUBLISHED EVERY MONDAY FROM
CHICAGO, ILLINOIS MARCH 12, 1888

EDITORIAL

THE DARK DAYS AHEAD

Rumors are spreading regarding the exclusion of Negro players from the game of baseball. Word around town, through the back alleys and around bars and men's sports clubs, is some team owners, managers, and players are quietly moving behind closed doors to prevent Negroes from playing professionally in the future. Worse still, some say this ban will affect current players who will be denied contract renewals in the coming seasons.

Many fear this powder keg is due to explode as organized boycotts against teams that field any Negro players are assembled and ready to go. Rumors are rapidly becoming fact as Cap Anson of the Chicago White Stockings publicly and proudly voiced such exclusionary views recently and attempted to enforce his beliefs by benching Henry Dupont and Sammy Hayes, two of the best outfielders in the game today, during a crucial game against crosstown rivals, the Riverside Rockets.

And when, responding to the cheers, he lightly doffed his hat,
No stranger in the crowd could doubt 'twas Casey at the bat.

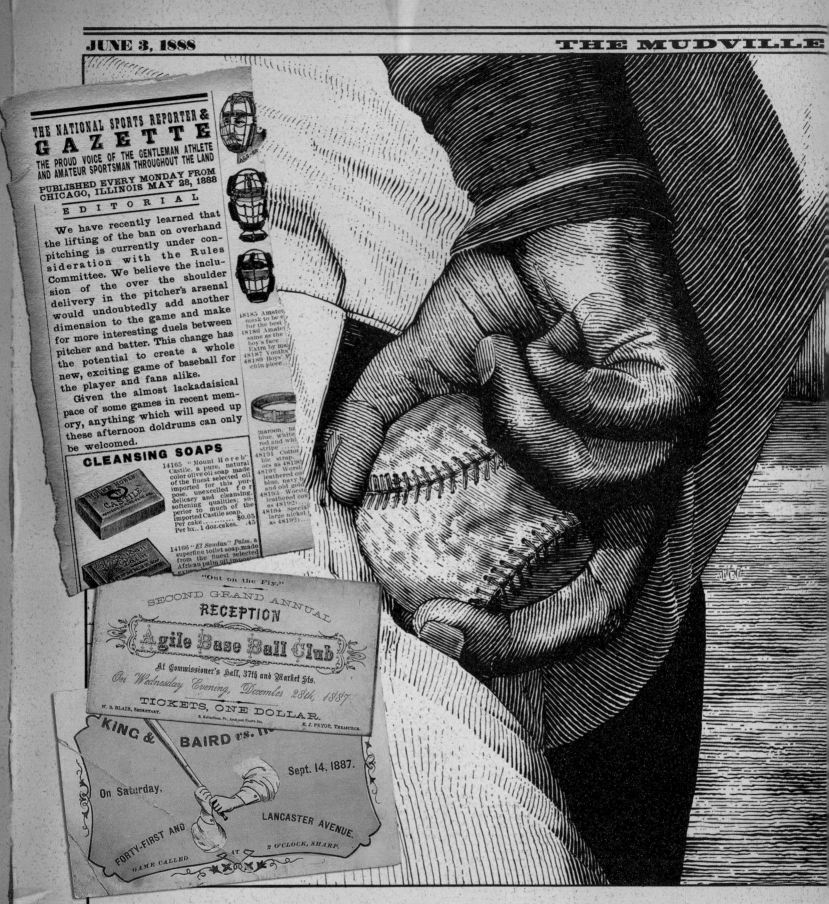

Ten thousand eyes were on him as he rubbed his hands with dirt;
Five thousand tongues applauded when he wiped them on his shirt.

P. Martin

Then while the writhing pitcher ground the ball into his hip, Defiance gleamed in Casey's eye, a sneer curled Casey's lip.

And now the leather-covered sphere came hurtling through the air,
And Casey stood a-watching it in haughty grandeur there.

PUBLISHED EVERY MON
CHICAGO, ILLINOIS

LETTERS TO THE EDIT

Sir:

I would like to r
disagree with your
absolutely absurd sugg
lifting the overhand
would be good for the
delivery has been ba
baseball for some time
good reason! Any thinking
should realize that the offense will
suffer greatly should the ban be
lifted and the game will be
stripped of any semblance of fair
play. With such an unlimited
sphere of delivery, along with the
added power put upon the ball, the
overhand pitch gives the defense
all the power.

The

Melville Center Celebration, June 3, 1888
ARTISTICVIEW

Balloon Inflation ceremony

only possible remedy for
this outrageous travesty of justice
would be to move the pitcher's
box back ten feet from its present
position. This would allow the
batter to have more time to react
and up the probability of actually
making contact with the ball.

Certainly, no serious fan of the
sport would deny that home runs
and line drives are what make
baseball exciting--no one goes to
the park to see strike outs and
no-hitters. Unless the overhand
pitch is coupled with the shifted
pitcher's box, reinstating the
overhand pitch will completely
ruin baseball. If it isn't broken,
gentlemen...Don't Try To Fix It!

C. Franceschelli

Close by the sturdy batsman the ball unheeded sped—
"That ain't my style," said Casey. "Strike one," the umpire said.

Roscript Finds a Defender in a
Liberal M.P.

Walking Down the Road, Cowie and
McQuaid Overtook Her.

From the benches, black with people, there went up a muffled roar,
Like the beating of the storm-waves on a stern and distant shore.

Debut of American Singers.
(Copyright.)
LONDON, June 2.—Howard Paul introduced two young American vocalists at the concert in St. James' Hall last evening. They were Mrs. Adelina Hibbard of New York and Miss Luelle Saunders of Hartford.

bitter enemy of organized labor.

SIXTY-SIX LASTERS QUIT.

Stowe, Bills & Hawley's Union Men Refuse to Work with Non-Unionists.

MARLBORO, June 2.—The trouble in the shoe factory of Stowe, Bills & Hawley in Hudson, between the Lasters' Union and

nevertheless served in two departments, and yet was able to make his address for Blaine, while Arthur was sulking under his defeat.

The silly plea that a convention of common sense men must decide against anybody whom the mugwumps do not insult and hate, shows how Gresham is growing, and there is some danger that the entire West may make his issue theirs, from East of the Ohio river off on the Allegheny chain

who will vote for him don't like Cleveland, there is nothing else to be done.

William Armstrong, postmaster of Cleveland, an old Democrat, remarked to Judge Thurman: "The Ohio delegates a few votes, I think, for Black; some for Stevenson, and a small number for Gray. But if this is sincere, bringing Thurman's name, of course there will be opposition to him in Ohio. It is, however, to understand the politics

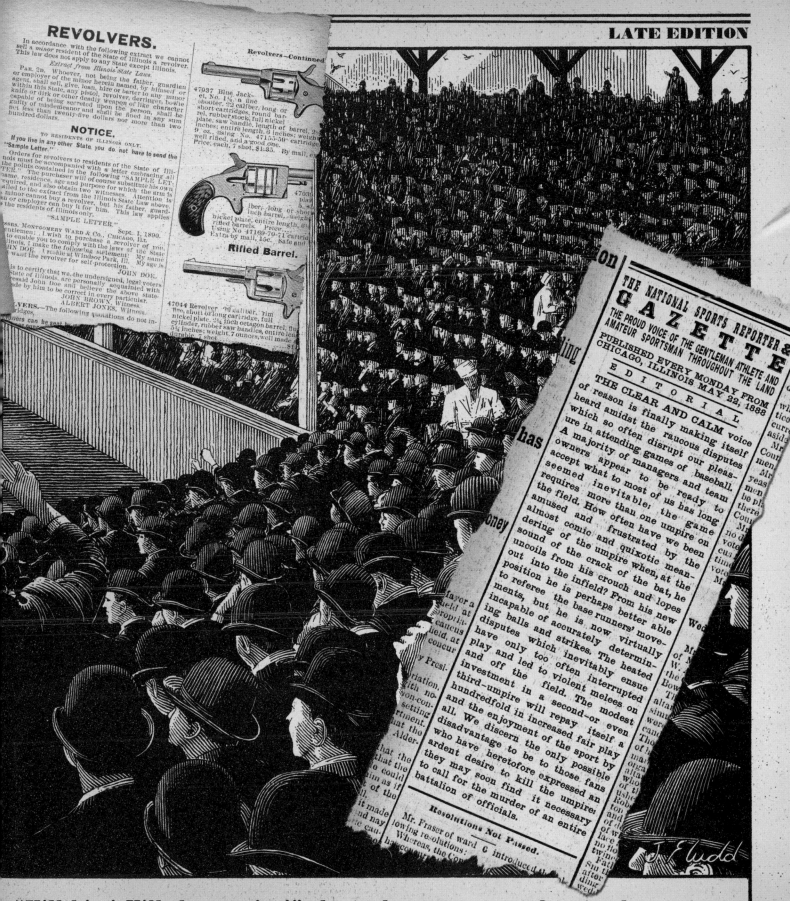

> "Kill him! Kill the umpire!" shouted some one on the stand;
> And it's likely they'd have killed him had not Casey raised his hand.

CASEY-MUDVILLE

COPYRIGHTED BY GOODWIN & CO., 1887.

GOODWIN & CO. New Y

Blake,
(3rd Base - Mudville)

KELLY,
(C. Boston)

BOSTON

With a smile of Christian charity great Casey's visage shone;
He stilled the rising tumult; he bade the game go on;

He signaled to the pitcher, and once more the spheroid flew;
But Casey still ignored it, and the umpire said, "Strike two."

MUDVILLE SCRIMMAGE AT MEMORIAL PARK

MAY 1888

"Fraud!" cried the maddened thousands, and echo answered fraud;
But one scornful look from Casey and the audience was awed.

display of tri-colored bunting formed an appropriate background for the designs in black and white. These consisted of the colors of the Honourable Artillery Company, the Ancients and the Old Guard, and a portrait of John Milton, a member of the Honourable Artillery Company of Lon-

Wedding at the Church of St. John the Evangelist.

Mrs. Helen Mixter of Beacon street, niece of Mrs. Nathaniel W. Curtis, and Randolph W. Appleton of New York were married at the Church of St. John the Evangelist, on

the slip.

IN HONOR OF R. D. SMITH.

Meeting of the Boston Bar to Take Action on His Death.

There was a meeting of the bar this morn-

brooks they may hold communion with daisies. Perhaps with Claribel and Lilian they will not have time to tell the wrong they have done their fellow by their actions. But time levels all the and the men unjustly treated may hope. All else I can say is that in the

Mudville 11; Salem, 7.

Mudville May 31.—Salem lost today's game on account of an unlucky error by Long in the first inning. Kiley was batted out of the box in the fourth. Burns was also batted hard. Mudville played greatly in the field, but one error, a base on balls, being made. Flynn did fine work in left field, and Rabensky and Casey fielded well. Casey's batting was a feature. The score:

LOWELL

	AB.	R.	BH.	TB.	PO.	A.	E.
Casey							
Rabensky							
Flynn							
Jones							
O'Toole							
Barrows							
Perrone							
Blake							
Cooney							
Total	44	11	15	26	27	15	

SALEM

	AB.	R.	BH.	TB.	PO.	A.	E.
Goodwin, 2b.							
Innes, c.f.							
Ray, s.s.							
Earle, c.							
Prince, 1b.							
Trask, l.f.							
Long, 3b.							
Kiley, p.							
Henry, r.f.							
Totals	41	7	17	23		7	10

Innings									
Lowell								0—11	
Salem								0— 7	

Earned runs—Lowell, 4; Salem, 5. Two-base hits—Quer, Prince, Earl, Kiley. Home runs—Quer, Henry, Polhemus, Kennedy. First base on balls—Burns, Kiley, 3. First base on errors—Lowell, 5. Struck out—by Kiley, 3; by Burns, Earle. Double plays—Ray, Long and Prince. Hit by pitched ball—Burns. Umpire—

Barrett

**They saw his face grow stern and cold, they saw his muscles strain,
And they knew that Casey wouldn't let that ball go by again.**

DUNLAP,
(CAPT, PITTSBURG)

The sneer is gone from Casey's lip, his teeth are clenched in hate;

MUDVILLE

PIONEER BASE BALL CLUB

T. Sutherland

He pounds with cruel violence his bat upon the plate.

And now the pitcher holds the ball, and now he lets it go,

And now the air is shattered by the force of Casey's blow.

g the Republicans a good deal of
le, if they had yet got down to seri-
y consider it. But I don't hear much
in either party a out the
perance matter this year. Now
then a Democrat will say
Republican friend that "your party will
only two issues after a time, prohibi-
and protection." But the che ar u-

peculiar aspects to the vice president situa-
tion. For a year there have been two or
three active and aggress ve can idates in
the field for this p ace, that is generally
unsought; but there has b en no national
interest in these r ther local characters
and their aspirations. Nobody cares particularly for Gray, who has been the lead-
ing candidate. He s not a figure in the

COLUMBUS, June 2.—A number of delegates to the Democratic national convention called at Senator Thurman's resid nce
this afternoon, prior to leaving for St. Louis,
but no meeting w s held relative to tak ng
a tion towards his support for vice president. Only about one-half the delegation
was here. Judy Sherman will not go to St.
Louis.

ance at the Country Club races yesterday,
accompanied by Lady Middleton.

Prominent among the military men at
Young's are General John H. Reed of Cotab
and Colonel Harry Hale of Bradford. Both
gentlemen attended the reception in Maso
Hall last nigl in honor of our English and

Oh, somewhere in this favored land the sun is shining bright;
The band is playing somewhere, and somewhere hearts are light;

SURE TO BE THURMAN.

ne of the Delegates All Pointing to Thurman's Nomination.

LOUIS, June 2.—The newspaper men about the only visitors in St. Louis who day any eager interest in the Demo-

possible. An Indianian whispered that Thurman's name and a speech at Indianapolis would do more good in Hoosierdom than Gray's nomination. Red bananas are beginning to wave in front of headquarters and Tammany will march behind this familiar symbol of the eminent snuff-taker of Columbus.

Just the same, it is a mighty cruel thing to

would add strength to the ticket, and would secure Indiana to the Democrats without a doubt. No formal action was taken, however, and the delegation will map out its course at a future meeting.

The name of Thurman of Ohio was mentioned, and while his past services to the party and to the country were highly and warmly commended, it was generally

Painters and plumbers now at wor

—Today is the day to sample celebrated ice cream, there is nothin

—Messrs. Hollis, Cobb & Co. ar with prosperity in a very substan at their new quarters at No. W street. The Tiner man and th lever are both catered to, a be bringing rapid returns from every ye

The two old Commonwealths

And somewhere men are laughing, and somewhere children shout;
But there is no joy in Mudville—mighty Casey has struck out.

TOM REED'S OPPONENT.

Mr. Emery Favors Cleveland and Expects to See Thurman Nominated.

SANFORD, Me., June 2.—Hon. William Emery, whom the Democrats of the first district will support for Congress next September, on being questioned by a Globe reporter regarding his opinions of the com...

EDITOR'S NOTE:

In order to achieve the feel of a newspaper published in the late Nineteenth Century, great care has been taken to use only fonts equivalent to those that might have been readily available to the compositor of a small town newspaper of the era.

We are particularly fortunate to have had as a resource the collection of historical fonts collected by the Walden Font Company of Winchester, Massachusetts.

Every reasonable attempt has been made to create a seamless tapestry of the real and the fictional, with the modern techniques of photo manipulation and the skill of a gifted designer permitting an unparalleled flexibility in interposing imaginary characters, names and memorabilia into a realistic setting.

The articles "reproduced" from periodicals such as The National Sports Reporter & Gazette and various newspapers in the Mudville area rolled off presses which exist only in the imagination of their creators. They do, however, seek to accurately reflect and articulate actual issues of the day.

It seems only fitting that the figure of Casey is so inextricably woven into the fabric of our history that the Library of Congress--that arbiter of last resort of the classification of books--should have formally and

Remingt
STANDARD

Typewriter.

WYCKOFF, SEAMANS & BENEDICT, 327 Broadway, New York, Boston, Mass.; Philadelphia, Pa.; Washington, D. C.; Baltimore, Md.; Chicago Ill.; St. Louis, Mo.; Indianapolis, Ind.; Minneapolis, Minn.; St. Paul, Minn.; Kansas City, Mo.; Denver, Col.; Cincinnati and Cleveland, O.; London, England.
NOTE.— *Our unqualified challenge for a test of all Writing Machines remains unaccepted. Send for copy if interested.*

permanently assigned to him a date of birth, of death, and a profession.

Casey stands as a heroic reminder that the blurring of fact and fancy, reality and imagination, resides at the core of the American experience.

The final images delivered to the printer were prepared entirely digitally: the artist's illustrations were scanned and then merged with the ancillary images which had been manipulated--or even created--digitally using a variety of graphics software programs

At 1 o
ing quiet
have appear
The Penns
tendered the gene
should at any time b
special train to bring Dr.
delphia to Washing on.

including Illustrator, Quark XPress, and Photoshop. A single illustrated spread may be the result of "sandwiching" as many as twenty layers of design elements: type, hand-drawn art, baseball ephemera, and background illustrations; the amount of data needed to describe even one such spread considerably exceeds the information required to print out a very generously-sized encyclopedia.

The black-and-white illustrations were drawn using pen, ink, and brush on white (uninked) scratch board. The newspaper and scrapbook background were created through a series of complex operations involving mirrored photocopies on acetate, 100% cotton-rag watercolor paper soaked in warm acetone baths and watercolors.